MYSTERIES OF THE VENUS PENTAGRAM

Workbook
2021-2022

Tashi Powers
Evolutionary Astrologer

Designed by **George Ozuna**

Independently Published 2021

Dear Toacha

♡ Thanks ♡

Tashi

Disclaimer:

The information in this book is given in good faith and intended for
information only. Neither author nor publisher can be held liable by any
person for any loss or damage whatsoever which may arise directly or
indirectly from the use of this book or any of the information therein.

Edited by Kevin Stein
Cover design: George Ozuna
Text design and layout by Lorena Mathendu
Gem consultation from Genna Howard
www.aquarianature.com

Tashi Powers © 2021
SECOND EDITION
ISBN: 978-1-7353264-3-6

Independently Published
California, United States of America

For information on this and other works visit
www.enlighteningtimes.com

Venus Gates Workbook

This astrological workbook is a companion to the author's previous work, Mysteries of the Venus Pentagram. It is dedicated to teaching seekers how to navigate and record their journey through the next two cycles in 2021 and 2022 of the Venus, Sun, and Moon Gates.

Both of these years include magical Pentagram Points that readers can use to greatly enhance their daily lives. They will also learn about the Venus Morning and Evening Star phases, as well as the dates of the Moon/Venus Gates.

Venus bestows incredible gifts to us all on her special alignment days, and to truly take advantage of her offerings, an attitude of gratitude will afford readers more than they ever imagined possible. Above all, this workbook serves as a guide on how to co-create with the Multi-verse. Using the wisdom of the Gates, spiritual seekers will see what is needed not only for their own best outcomes, but for the Greater Good.

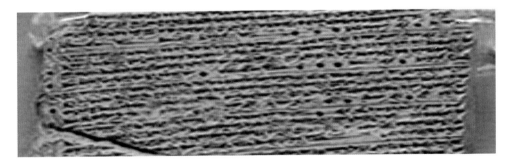

Venus Tablet of Ammisaduqa 720-740 B.C.

This book is dedicated to:

....all my fellow students of Evolutionary Astrology.

....all fans of Venus and the God/Goddess/All that is.

....any soul wanting to learn how to co-create with the Cosmos.

AUTHOR'S FORWARD

Little is really taught to us about the marvelous planetary system that guides us in our lives on Earth. And yet we are guided by a predictable clock, that is run by the Cosmos.

We are a part of a life cycle where we gather, organize, and deliver as well as set it up and pay it off—this is the Karmic accounting that is revealed in a picture or chart of the sky at the moment of our birth.

My tribe of evolutionary astrologers—is a community that dives deep into ancient texts, charts of events, those of our friends, family, clients, celebrities, great thinkers, and the various moments of our lives—to study how the planets operate.

It is both complex and mysterious since we work with cycles that are within greater cycles.

As the planets orbit our Sun, they make astounding, beautiful, sacred geometric circles, spirals, and arcs as shown in the image on the next page.

My many friends around the planet who have helped me along the way, who kept the passion to know the Stars and Planets as living beings—are all in my heart. I thank you and I owe you a debt of gratitude.

In this life, I have studied and learned mainly from these Astrology teachers: Jeffrey Wolf Green, Marion March, Ed Steinbrecher, Judy Johns, and Dane Rudhyar.

Now I have matured to have a world full of students of my own, who are also my best teachers. I like to say we are all each other's teachers.

A team has sprung up or should I say, arrived by design—who now collaborate to help with my astrological work. In particular, this workbook has been birthed with the support of Kevin Stein, Genna Howard, Lorena Mathendu, Mark Flaisher, and my marketing crew at mPulse.

Kevin Stein is my publishing partner and the voice inside my head that reminds me of the wonderful Aquarian aspect of my life, He is a guiding light as I strive to leave a legacy of astrological knowledge. He keeps it real and also reminds me that I am but a messenger. He has envisioned, edited, and conceived this workbook with me.

My partner and protégé, Genna Howard, has lovingly helped me study the 15 Venus Moon Gates in the book, as she is learning to delineate the future, herself. She has consulted on the gemstones in the Workbook and is also the fine artist who creates our Vastu hangers.

Lorena Mathendu showed up through divine Angelic intervention to help me with Adobe CSS, and brilliantly provided this book with some new layouts.

Venus Pentagram Trajectory
Illustrated by George Ozuna

Now I have matured to have a world full of students of my own, who are also my best teachers. I like to say we are all each other's teachers.

A team has sprung up or should I say, arrived by design—who now collaborate to help with my Astrological work. In particular, this workbook has been birthed with the support of Kevin Stein, Genna Howard, Lorena Mathendu, Mark Flaisher, and my marketing crew at mPulse.

Kevin Stein is my publishing partner and the voice inside my head that reminds me of the wonderful Aquarian aspect of my life.

He is a guiding light as I strive to leave a legacy of Astrological knowledge.

He keeps it real and also reminds me that I am but a messenger. He has envisioned, edited, and conceived this workbook with me.

My partner and protégé, Genna Howard, has lovingly helped me study the fifteen Venus Moon Gates in the book, as she is learning to delineate the future, herself. She has consulted on the gemstones in the Workbook and is also the fine artist who makes our Vastu hangers.

Lorena Mathendu showed up through divine Angelic intervention to help me with Adobe CSS, and brilliantly, provided this book with some new layouts.

George Ozuna's original graphic designs and layouts here, and in the companion book—Mysteries of the Venus Pentagram.

Mark Flaisher is our newest graphic designer who has an aesthetic flair informed by his long-standing experience in technology and software design.

I have so much gratitude in my heart for the team at RaMa, especially Gurujagat and Joanna Pitt, who collaborate in the best Aquarian way to keep the Venus Gates in front of their audience of the Dharma.

I cherish the ability to share my passion for Astrology with you all. My fellow yogis and meditators are my "Ride or Die."

Finally, my child, Madison, is my raison d'etre, in addition to being my Guru, and is the great soul, of course, to whom I owe everything.

So Much Love to us All,

Tashi Powers, Evolutionary Astrologer

TABLE OF CONTENTS

Contents

THE FIERY PENTAGRAMS

The stylized diagram of the five sequential Venus cycles shown here form a pentagram made by the five points of its Sun/Venus conjunctions. This is a symbol found in ancient Vedic mythology and all mystical traditions.

In the Vedic Astrological lore, the Holy Kumaris are considered Promethean beings who were thought to have used these Sun/Venus conjunctions to give infant humanity the spark of intelligence, and the seed of individuality–for better and for worse.

In Natural Law, the Venus Pentagram Points (VPP) are empowering points of intelligence in your chart. These Venus/Sun conjunctions in your personal horoscope highlight the place where you nurture the high magnetic frequency of Venus, which is regularly bestowed via transits into your chart.

This Link has a beautiful rendition of the pattern which Venus and the Earth make moving around the Sun as they form the Venus Pentagram Mandala. ☯

https://astrobutterfly.com/2017/03/22/venus-conjunct-sun-a-new-venus-cycle-a-rebirth-of-the-hearth/

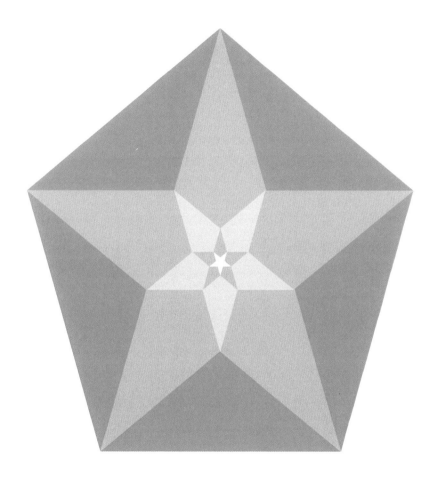

Illustration by George Ozuna

GEOMETRIC PENTAGRAMS

FOUND IN NATURE

It regenerates itself, creating one pentagram after another inside itself. By joining all five points of the pentagram, a new pentagram forms in the middle, and this goes on forever—forming the Venus Pentagram Mandala.

How eternal and regenerative is our love force? The more love we give, the more we receive.

Each Sun/Venus Pentagram Point (VPP) affords another chance to re-generate the following Venusian principles and trends:

Love
Self-Worth
Relationships
Societal Mores
Economic Reform
Humanistic Values

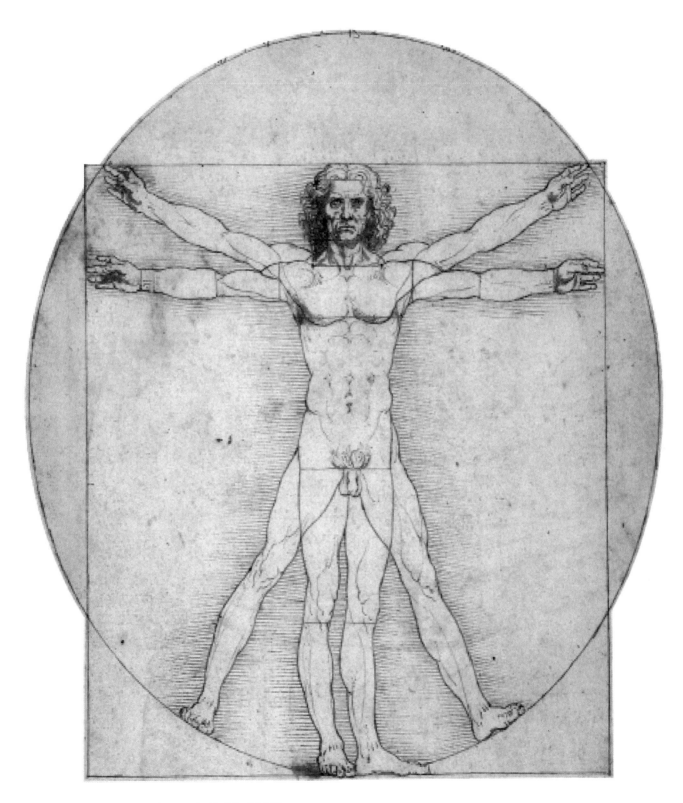

Leonardo Da Vinci 1490
Drawing

THE VITRUVIAN MAN

The Venus 5 Pentagram Points have been connected to the Vitruvian Man.

See how the drawing by philosopher and artist, Leonardo Da Vinci incorporates the Five-Pointed Star.

Perhaps Leonardo Da Vinci was portraying a heliocentric-based universe when he created L'Uomo Vitruviano around 1490 during the Italian Renaissance.

The drawing, which is in pen and ink on paper, depicts a man in two superimposed positions with his arms and legs apart and inscribed in a circle and square. ☯

Source: Wikipedia

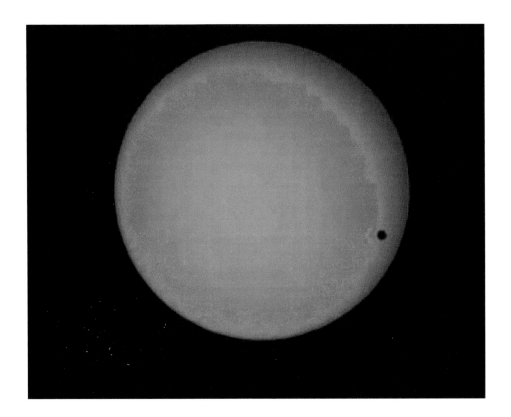

These long cycles are called The Transit of Venus, and show major historic changes as our tools and values both evolve during the Transit of Venus over the Sun.

NATURAL LAWS OF THE VENUS CYCLES

SUPERIOR CONJUNCTION

The Venus/Sun superior conjunction occurs when Venus is behind the Sun. Venus is moving in direct motion.

INFERIOR CONJUNCTION

The Venus/Sun inferior conjunction occurs when Venus is between the Earth and the Sun. Venus is moving in retrograde motion. In both cases, Venus is not visible in most of the lower latitudes.

MAXIMUM ELONGATION

Occurs 216 days after the superior conjunction.

MAXIMUM BRIGHTNESS

Occurs 36 days following maximum elongation.

The Venus Pentagram Points form a Pentagram Star that revolves within an oval in a clockwise direction. The pentagram is formed after 5 cycles of Venus/Sun conjunctions in approximately 8 year cycles.

Venus/Sun conjunctions repeat in 5 cycle sets completing an entire round once every 1,215 years.

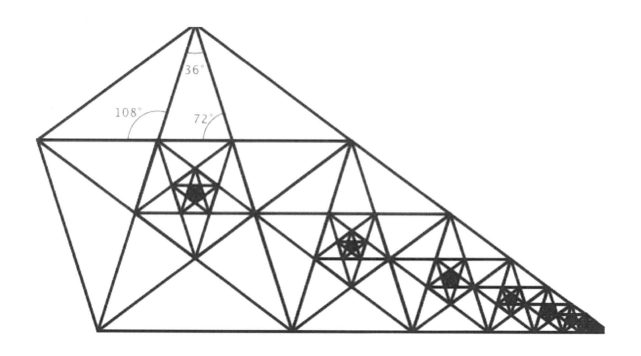

VENUS PENTAGRAM POINTS

Keep an eye on the changing VPP every 9 months and see how it brings people and new values into your world.

The VPP also changes the social climate around us and these big changes are part of at least an 8 year cycle.

The five signs of the Pentagram Mandala correspond to eight-year periods in which these same five signs are repeated.

There are also years when the signs change and these are break-out changing years in society.

The Fiery Pentagrams are given here for the years 2021-2025. The signs are Aries, Gemini, Leo, Libra, and Capricorn.

Libra is a new pentagram, which means we have never had one. We can anticipate new ways of relating. I am praying for an upgrade of the *two-way street*. A three-way street of give-and-take which includes the support of the Cosmos.☯

Plot your VPP using these links:

https://sophiavenus.com/pdf/FindYourVenusStarPoint.pdf
https://eclipse.gsfc.nasa.gov/transit/catalog/VenusCatalog.html ☯

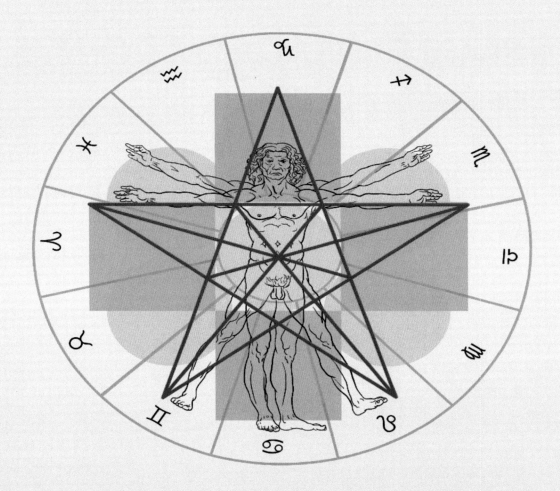

CURRENT
VENUS PENTAGRAM POINT DATES

JUL 03 2020 INFERIOR CONJUNCTION   13° Gem 36'

MAR 26 2021 SUPERIOR CONJUNCTION 5° Ar 50'

Jan 8 2022 INFERIOR CONJUNCTION   18°Cp43' R

Oct 22 2022 SUPERIOR CONJUNCTION   29°Li26' D

Aug 13 2023 INFERIOR CONJUNCTION   20°Le28' R

Jun 4 2024 SUPERIOR CONJUNCTION   14°Ge29' D

Mar 22 2025 INFERIOR CONJUNCTION   02°Ar39' R

8 Year Transit of Venus		8 Year Transit of Venus	
Dec 7, 1631	Dec 4, 1639	Jun 6, 1761	Jun 3, 1769	Dec 9, 1874	Dec 6, 1882

8 Year Transit of Venus

243 Years

243 Years

The rare 243-year Venus Transit cycles have two occurrences of the major alignment of Venus with her Nodes.

This line-up occurs when an 8-year transit of Venus lines up with a 243-year transit.

A transit of Venus occurs when the planet Venus moves directly between the Sun and the Earth.

This causes a small obscuring of the solar disk when the planet Venus can be seen as a small black object moving across the surface of the Sun.

8 Year Transit of Venus

| Jun 8, 2004 | Jun 6, 2012 | Dec 11, 2117 | Dec 6, 2125 | Jun 6, 2247 | Jun 6, 2255 |

8 Year Transit of Venus

8 Year Transit of Venus

243 Years

243 Years

These Venus transits across the Sun are visible in pairs of 8-years. The most recent occurred in the period between 2004-2012—which is the tail end of the 1761 longer cycle and the middle of the 1874 cycle.

We are living in consequential times, having experienced the current Venus transit from 2004-2012.

The Mayan Astrological calendar mentions the period from 2012-2024 to be a distinctive shift in global consciousness.

Examples of the last Transit of Venus:

English Renaissance 1630s

Industrial Revolution 1760s

Telephone Invented 1880

Internet goes mobile 2007-2012

The next Transit of Venus occurs in 2117.

TRANSITIONAL DATES

Oct 22 2022—the new Libra Star at 29°Libra 26'D Evening Star

Oct 23 2026—the last Scorpio Star is ending at 00°Scorpio 45'Rx.

The next VPP BEGINS OCT 22, 2022 at 29 Libra.

The Libra Star begins before the Scorpio one fades out, so expect some Scorpio intensity, greed, and coercion as Scorpio power struggles fade away.

Libra broadens our perspective as we compare and contrast ourselves in relationship to a variety of people.

On a global level, this Libra Pentagram many bring strategic partnerships, and a new level of global cooperation.

2023-2024—Pluto's entrance into Aquarius shifts us to the realization we must collaborate to survive as individuals as it takes us all into collective consciousness.

2018-2022—These years will be transitional times as the Scorpio Pentagram point shifts to a Libra Pentagram.

1926-2018—The fading Scorpio Star at 03°Scorpio 06' Rx began Nov 21, 1926 as an Evening Star.

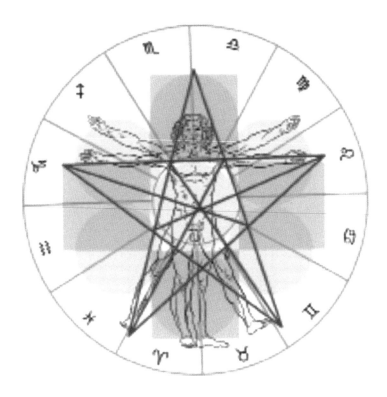

TRANSITIONAL PENTAGRAM POINTS

On Oct 22, 2022 a New Venus Pentagram Point (VPP) will be at 29° Libra 26' appearing as an Evening Star. Scorpio has not quite faded yet, as the last Scorpio VPP occurs on Oct 23, 2026, at 00° Scorpio 45' Rx. The next Libra VPP is on Oct 20, 2030 and is also a superior conjunction. The first Rx, inferior conjunction of Venus and the Sun in Libra does not occur until Oct 21, 2034 at 28 Libra 22 Rx.

It is my prayer that as the Scorpio VPP fades, we will have learned lessons of sharing, caring and inclusion. If as Yogi Bhajan, a mystic from India, stated: "The Age of Aquarius begins in 2035," then this new VPP in Libra in 2034 is another indication.

In Libra, we learn balance. Over any given lifetime, we are presented with various sensory experiences, which are the litmus tests for our interactions with others.

We eventually learn to look at the reflection of others as a mirror image of ourselves.

Venus Pentagram Trajectory
Illustration by George Ozuna

- VENUS KEYWORDS—Beauty, Sensory Pleasure, Music, Art, Money, Possessions, Income, Material Values

- INNER SIDE OF VENUS—TAURUS—Relationship with Self. Correlates to Venus Morning Star

- OUTER SIDE OF VENUS—LIBRA—Relationships with Others. Correlates to Venus Evening Star

- FEMININE PRINCIPLE—Nature-Based, Interconnected Existence of all Creation, which is the Creative Vessel of Life that Contains, Nurtures, and Protects

- RELATIONSHIPS—A Variety of Relationships (Marriage is Scorpio), Business Relationships, Partnerships, and Counseled/Counselor Relationships

- COOPERATION—Listening to the Other, Diplomacy, Agreements, Compromise, and Alliance

- NATURAL LAW—Sharing, Caring, and Inclusion

- INTERACTION—Socializing, Relating, Comparing, Evaluating, Give-and-Take, Reflection, and Mirroring

CYCLES, PHASES & STAGES

Use the workbook at the end of this volume to plot the positions and movement of Venus from Morning Star to Evening Star.

Access the links to the ephemerides to look up the movement of Venus at the time of your birth.

By studying the phase and gate of the Moon/Venus descent or ascent of your natal Venus phase at birth, you will know more about where you are in this larger cycle of evolutionary momentum.

What kind of Kumari Kiss did you come to Earth to receive?

The early Indigo's of the Pluto in Leo generation gave us the soundtrack, music, and inspiration to Love each other. The Beatles said it well: "All you need is love, love is all you need." The band began in 1960 as the Pluto/Uranus trigger of the Aquarian Age was unfolding.

Those born in the 1960s with the Pluto/Uranus conjunction in Virgo — came for the evolution/revolution, and to help birth the Aquarian Age.

The children of the 1970s with their Neptunes in Sagittarius are here to re-think limiting beliefs and align with Natural Law.

Those born in the 1980s, came for the Capricorn stellium which is still bringing a New World Order.

The children of the 1990s are here with Pluto in Scorpio to keep the intensity for change, evolution, growth, and co-creation real.

The children born in the 2000's are the new crystalline souls whose radiant body is full of Pluto in Sagittarius know-how.☯

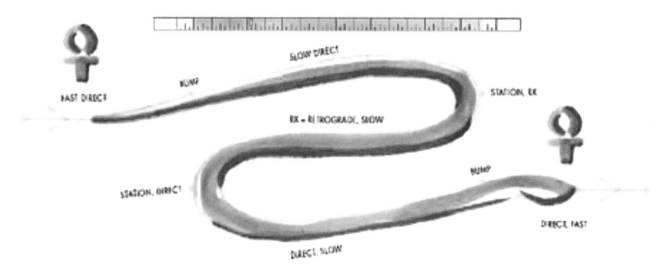

SLOW DIRECT

BUMP

FAST DIRECT

STATION, RX

RX - RETROGRADE, SLOW

STATION, DIRECT

BUMP

DIRECT, FAST

DIRECT, SLOW

Venus Retrograde
Illustration by George Ozuna

The retrogrades of Venus slow us down in order to review our choices.

The retrograde also allows us to discover how to make better decisions. As a result we are able to resolve the dynamics that block our evolutionary path forward.

During the Morning Star retrograde phase, we are given the opportunity to improve our self-esteem. We may also have to look at rash actions, impulsive actions, and judgment calls.

In the Evening Star retrograde phase, we can make better choices to improve or repair our relationships. We may be also able to better cooperate, and more easily accept concessions and agreements.

Venus Retrograde occurs every 18 months and lasts for approximately 40 days (see table).

VENUS RETROGRADE

- Venus Rx, with its Uranian flavor, may correlate to unusual relationships and experiences.

- Depending on the sign and phases, it is possible for Venus retrograde to indicate changes in behavior that look like a sharp left turn.

- People show up who enable us to re-experience unresolved relationship issues.

- During Venus Rx, we are more likely to be able to break away from our consensus conditioning.

- Wherever we have suppressed our desires, the retrograde phenomenon will assist us to access the subconscious and sort out its repressed contents.

- When Venus is retrograde, we are reliving, repeating, and taking care of the unfinished business in key karmic relationships.

- Conditions will be set up that emphasize our own individuation.

- We often have to release traumas related to sado-masochistic components of patriarchal domination/submission scenarios.

- Violation of the feminine—as the patriarchy grinds to a slow end—will continue to require examination and confrontation. ☯

Based on the Burney Babylon1800-1750 Relief
by George Ozuna

VENUS EVENING STAR

Venus begins her ascent after she forms a new Pentagram Point and appears as an Evening Star.

In the Sumerian myth, Venus ascends back up through the *Seven Gates*. When ancient astrologers observed Venus setting in the evening sky, they noticed that she rises a little higher each evening.

The ascent is a period of personal empowerment.

According to myth, Venus was ascending after accomplishing the intentions she initiated on her descent a year earlier.

I have provided a table of these dates to help you observe and correlate these Seven Gates with the ascent of Venus.

Use the tables of the Seven Gates to journal your memories.

The journal pages offer keywords to help you with your own self-empowering passage. ☯

THE CYCLES OF VENUS

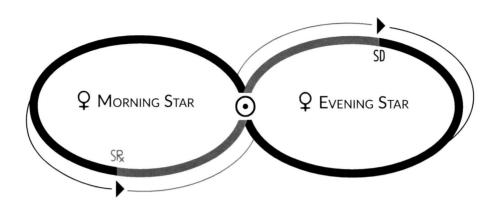

VENUS ES IN SUNLIGHT

During the first several weeks of its Evening Star phase, the light of Venus is occluded in the solar glare and will soon begin her ascent phase.

SUPERIOR CON-JUNCTION

The Venus/Earth superior conjunction occurs when Venus is behind the Sun. During the Venus ES phase, Venus is moving at or near maximum velocity.

A NEW VPP FORMS

A VPP Star forms again at superior conjunction when Venus is direct and moving through the zodiac—near its maximum speed. Once again, when the Sun and Venus meet at the same degree of the zodiac and form a conjunction, we receive another wave of etheric Venus light.

This occurs in the full phase of the 584 day Venus Cycle, thus compelling us to complete social tasks and work on how we relate more objectively to the world and others.

Venus Sets after the Sun = Evening Star She is visible after Sunset. She ascends a little higher each night.

VENUS EVENING STAR

A few weeks after the Sun and Venus meet in superior conjunction, Venus emerges on the other side of the Sun, appearing as the Evening Star.

THE SEVEN GATES

At each of the Venus ES gates, we integrate values and insights into our emotional body, correlating to the Venus/Moon conjunctions.

The ES Seven Gates correlate to the balsamic phase. The events and experiences of the past year's descent cycle has given us a wider perspective as we choose the path forward.

Evening Star periods are social in nature due to the opposition of Venus and the Sun. and thus, they may feel like a more deliberate and goal-oriented period.

The events and experiences of the past year's descent cycle has given us a wider perspective as we choose the path forward.

VENUS ES RX

Venus ES spends 40 days in retrograde motion just before the Inferior Conjunction. She switches from ES to MS during that time.

TRANSITS

During the ES ascent direct, we are likely to be extroverted. It is a time of building relationships throughout the seven new ascent Venus-Moon conjunctions of the balsamic phase.

Those who are successful in finding their authentic voice are often influencers if that is within their soul's purpose. ☯

THE CYCLES OF VENUS

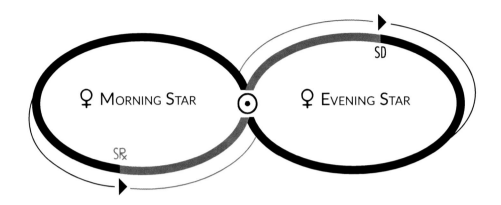

VENUS MORNING STAR

Venus begins her retrograde after maximum brilliance and spends a total of 40 days as she transitions from ES to MS.

INFERIOR CONJUNCTION

...occurs when Venus is between the Earth and the Sun.

The first part of the morning star phase occurs while Venus is retrograde, and it is therefore a time of self-authentication. We must now disengage and let go of the values that no longer serve our soul's growth. Venus retrograde correlates to a time for maximum individuation as we are less connected to consensus values. We are now likely to overthrow those social norms to which others adapt easily.

A NEW VPP FORMS

...at the inferior conjunction of Venus/Sun.

The mythic Kiss of the Kumari brings a gift of light from the fiery interaction of Venus and the Sun. It helps us with the descent ahead where we discover how to disengage and let go.

VENUS MS DIRECT

Venus MS direct is infused with light as she reappears courageously as an Evening Star.

The descent of Venus occurs after Venus continues her direct motion and she now meets the Moon seven times—thus the Seven Gates.

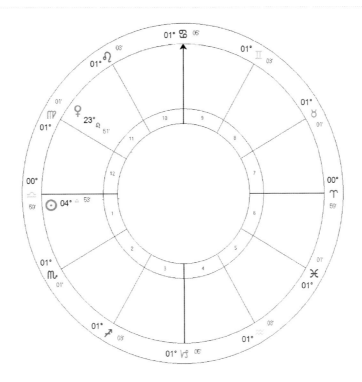

Venus rises before the Sun = Morning
Star She is visible before sunrise.

THE SEVEN GATES

...represent the seven stages of growth wherein we release old values. The breakthrough occur around the Venus/Moon conjunctions.

This is the gibbous phase of Venus.

Forward evolutionary motion must match inner growth. Inner growth must align personal desires to your deepest inner desire.

2020's Morning Star descent gates brought the "Black Lives Matter" front and center.

Hordes of people all over the world responded to the clarion call of the Morning Star.

VENUS MS TRANSITS

If you can see the morning sky, you can observe Venus as she descends lower and lower in the sky, eventually fading from view. Intentions are creation. Sow the seeds of dreams descending into matter, over this 544-day cycle.

During the seven Venus/Moon conjunctions, we engage and mature as we pass their tests.

These Moon/Venus conjunctions also correspond with increased activity of Schuman Resonance waves.

I always find luck is flowing from the Venus Gates.

We have provided a workbook that prompts you to journal your path to self-discovery! ☯

VENUS MORNING STAR

The *Myth of Inanna*, an ancient Sumerian myth, relates the visible and invisible passage of Venus as the story of the Goddess Inanna, the "Queen of Heaven."

We are told of her journey as she descends to attend the funeral of her sister's husband. Her sister, Ershkigal, rules as the Queen of the Underworld.

To begin her passage, she must purify herself to enter the underworld. As she descends through each of the Seven Gates towards the superior conjunction, Inanna must release attachments to all of her belongings. The seven gates are interpreted by some astrologers to a healing of the seven chakras.

When she disappears as a Morning Star, the myth equates this to her arrival in the underworld where she is killed by her sister.

This patriarchal take of women/hysteria and drama is a picture of dis-empowering the feminine.

Venus actually disappears into sunlight—with rebirth ahead.

As Venus moves out of the solar glare, our radiant body has been magnetized to shine brightly.☯

Based on the Burney Babylon1800-1750 Relief
by George Ozuna

Part Four Workbook

2021 Workbook

The following tables are for 2021 for the descent of Venus as the planet transitions from Morning Star to Evening Star:

Venus as an Evening Star moves from 04 Gemini to 23 Capricorn, once again aligning with Pluto in Capricorn in the winter of 2021. However, Jupiter and Saturn are now in Aquarius.

Aquarius shows us new way to live. Pluto leaving Capricorn in 2023-2024 will create world government alliances.

Venus emerges from a period of solar immersion from Feb 13 to Mar 25th, 2021. This is the time to meditate and magnetize your radiant body.

As she leaves from her Morning Star phase conjoining the Sun on March 25, 2021 and forming a new pentagram star at 06 Aries, we begin a fiery year ready to put hard-fought for Morning Star freedoms into the wisdom body of the Evening Star.

We will be using the Gates to integrate new principles into full effect in society at large. This year there are 8 gates.

The 8 Gates begin after Venus rises as an evening star on May 4th 2021, and she repeats many of the gates of 2020.

Venus's Nodes remain in Gemini this entire year. This will create enhanced communication, new ideas, and a desire to align with Gaia and a better grasp of her Natural Law.

To survive in the emerging New World Order, we must collaborate, work for peace with the environment, and the greater good of humanity. It takes the 12 years that Pluto will be moving through Aquarius for this vision to stabilize by 2036. ☯

THE VENUS MOON GATES OF VENUS EVENING STAR 2021

1st GATE—MAY 12 2021 — 04°GEMINI ♊
NAME THE REALITY - Classify, Identify & Categorize

Venus now travels again through the same Venus Gates as 2020. As the North Node of the Moon is also traveling in Gemini, we have an overwhelming need to integrate and use the information that can change all our lives for the better. This month is the best for all communications. Digital, technological, and printed gifts aligned with Natural Law will become available to all during this Gemini "Information Gate."

2nd GATE—JUNE 12 2021 — 11°CANCER ♋
SOCIAL CHANGE - Self-Reliance & Self-Sufficiency

As we emerge from the cocoon of 2020, our desire to mature and improve the world is ongoing. Find your place in the collective spirit of change so that you can become a part of the solution. New jobs will likely emerge as society tackles climate issues and saving the planet.

3rd GATE—JULY 12 2021 18°— LEO ♌
SELF-ACTUALIZING PURPOSE

Our collective evolution continues to require us to practice kindness as we deal with huge societal issues. We must draw on our inner strength and use our Leonean personal will forces. Many will now bring a focus to socially relevant themes through their personal talents. A tense T-square brings us to a crisis in values, while shining a light on economic solutions. Strengthen yourself and others with acts of kindness.

4h GATE—AUG 11 2021— 24°VIRGO ♍
HEALING CRISIS - Service to the Greater Good

Virgo brings a focus on self-improvement. We must overcome bad habits. Analysis/paralysis due to over thinking, worry, and self-indulgent negativity can be changed if you now use this Gate to practice complimenting reality instead of complaining about it. This Gate aspects Neptune, Pallas Athena, Chiron, and Vesta. Find gratitude for the blessings that are yet to come. Witness how everything serves your own evolution.

5th GATE—SEP 10 2021—29°LIBRA ♎
END OF AN ERA - "We" Consciousness

Libra is a time when our consciousness shifts from I to We. We can discover stability through relationships, work, and self-mastery. This is a big push to be the best you can be. Humility will save you from humiliation.

6th GATE—OCT 09 2021—2°SAGITTARIUS ♐
KARMIC ACCOUNTING - Natural Law

This Gate brings our hidden strengths to the foreground. With Saturn and Jupiter, we are making steps to align ourselves with a higher good through teaching others, learning more ourselves, and becoming a living expression of collective unity.

7th GATE—NOV 8-2021—2°CAPRICORN ♑
COLLECTIVE UNITY - World Government

Pluto brings an opportunity to have an experience of aligning with the Cosmos. You are an interdependent part of the whole. As such, you possess an individuating liberty as well as your own voice. Now it's time to "sing in the choir." Collaborate if you wish to have a better life.

8th GATE—DEC 6-2021—23°CAPRICORN ♑
WORLD SOUL - Maturity

A new world is being created as the collective emerges from the rabbit hole we fell into when we forgot to see ourselves as inhabitants of Gaia—a living planet. We are now moving towards a realization of our multidimensional reality, and a path of sharing, caring and inclusion. This Gate aligned with Pluto/Venus/Moon provides us with a chance to either progress or digress.

♈ Aries	♌ Leo	♐ Sagittarius
♉ Taurus	♍ Virgo	♑ Capricorn
♊ Gemini	♎ Libra	♒ Aquarius
♋ Cancer	♏ Scorpio	♓ Pisces

Vastu Gems 2021

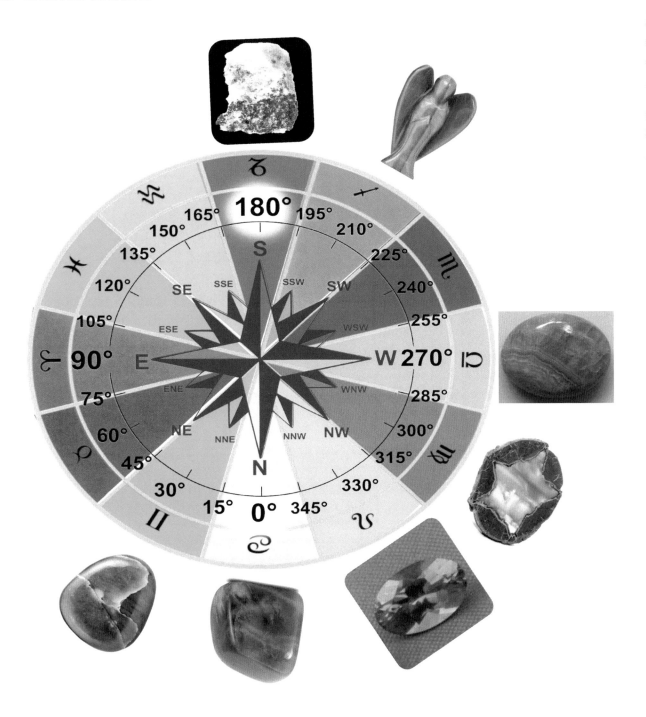

You can wear gems for the corresponding Venus gate, For example, place a Green Jade, Citrine, or Malachite in the compass area for Gemini, as shown above, until the next Gate (see chart for dates).

Vastu hangers for each sign available through:

and www.enlighteningtimes.com and www.aquarianature.com

The following are the signs which have Venus Gates in 2021.

Below is a Table of Gems that corresponds to the compass positions of the astrological Sun signs.

The compass provided on the previous page aligns the Sign of the Venus Gate and those Gems used in Vastu to connect to the Gate.

You can wear, hang, and place these gems. For more information about Gems, visit our website: www.enlighteningtimes.com

Gate	Compass	Use these Ideas to Journal	Gem
Gate 1 Gemini	015° - 045°	Describe how you walk your talk.	Green Jade, Malochite, Green Jasper
Gate 2 Cancer	015°-345°	Describe in what areas you would like to be more emotionally self-sufficient.	Peach Moonstone, Pearl, Seashell
Gate 3 Leo	315°- 345°	Describe how you can use your love to benefit others.	Sunstone, Amber, Citrine, Desert Rose
Gate 4 Virgo	285°- 315°	Describe how complimenting instead of complaining helps your life.	Agate, Himalayan Salt Rocks,Green Tourmaline
Gate 5 Libra	255°- 285°	Describe your "three-way street" in relationships: How do you include the Divine as you give and take?	Rose Quartz,Pink Chalcedony,Raspberry Tourmaline
Gate 6 Sagittarius	195°- 225°	Describe how your understanding is compassionate.	Tigers Eyes Lemon Quartz, Yellow Kunzite
Gate 7 & 8 Capricorn	165°- 195°	Describe where you demonstrate self-mastery	Lapis Lazuli, Obsidian, Blue Topaz, Howlite,

GEMS TO USE

REMEDIES

PLACEMENTS

THOUGHTS

EXPERIENCES

ASCENT OF VENUS
EVENING STAR

SUPERIOR CONJUNCTION	Mar 26 2021	5°♈50'D	♀ ☌ ☉ DIRECT
EVENING RISE	May 4 2021	23°♉'47' D	EVENING STAR
SEVEN GATES	May—Dec 2021	4°♊—23°♑'	☽ ☌ ♀
GREATEST ELONGATION	Oct 29 2021	23°♐35'D	♀☉ DISTANCE 47° 02'
GREATEST BRILLIANCE	Dec 7 2021	23°♑54'D	SLOWING DOWN
VENUS RETROGRADE	Dec 19 2021	26°♑29'R	♀ ℞
EVENING SET	Jan 3 2022	22°♑09'D	♀ SETS W
INFERIOR CONJUNCTION	Jan 9 2022	18°♑43'R	RX NEW PENTAGRAM
MORNING RISE	Jan 14 2022	15°♑42'R	MORNING STAR
VENUS DIRECT	Jan 29 2022	11°♑04'	FORWARD

☌ 00 DEGREES   CONJUNCTION

EVENING STAR GATES 2022
VENUS MOON CONJUNCTIONS

Evening Star	Heliacal Rise	May 04,21
Moon Venus Conjunctions		
Ascent	May 2021	to Dec 6,21
♀☌☽ Gate 1	**5/12/2021**	04 ♊ 43' D
♀☌☽ Gate 2	**6/12/2021**	11 ♋ 53' D
♀☌☽ Gate 3	**7/12/2021**	18 ♌ 29'D
♀☌☽ Gate 4	**8/11/2021**	24 ♍ 21'D
♀☌☽ Gate 5	**9/10/2021**	29 ♎ 14'D
♀☌☽ Gate 6	**10/09/2021**	2 ♐ 33'D
♀☌☽ Gate 7	**11/08/2021**	2 ♑ 36'D
♀☌☽ Gate 8	**12/06/21**	23 ♑ 37'D

2022 WORKBOOK

The following are the tables for 2022 for the ascent of Venus as the planet transitions from Morning Star to Evening Star.

These specific tables which we have provided will assist you in journaling about your experiences as Venus moves through the 8 Gates of the gibbous, evening star phase.

These Evolutionary Astrology keywords are provided to help you tune-in to the Natural Law behind the movement of the Moon and Venus.

The 8 Gates begin after Venus rises as an Evening Star on May 4th, 2021, and she repeats many of the Gates of 2020.

Venus's nodes remain in Gemini this entire year, continuing to bolster communication, expansion of thought, and an ability to align with the values of Natural Law.

The Evening Star in 2022 begins in Libra, which is the first pentagram in Libra.

The First Gate of 2022 has a Venus/Moon/Mars/Pluto conjunction in Capricorn, reminiscent of March, 2020. Collective evolution and collaborative collective governance may be unfolding. ☯

THE VENUS MOON GATES MORNING STAR 2022

1st GATE—FEB 27 2022—24°CAPRICORN ♑
WORLD COLLABORATION - SELF MASTERY

This Gate involves aspects of building a collaborative reality. In order to further the Greater Good—catch the wave that takes you to the shores of your creative, inspired, visionary leadership abilities.

2nd GATE—MARCH 28 2022 — 21°AQUARIUS ♒
COMMUNITY - SHARE, CARE, INCLUDE

If we collaborate and find a way to share, care, and include others, collective energetics will reward us. The greedy will now deal with setbacks. This is a pivotal Gate and you must be diligent, responsible, and socially-minded.

3rd GATE—APRIL 27 2022—23°PISCES ♓
UNITY CONSCIOUSNESS – "WE" CONSCIOUSNESS

This portal connects with Jupiter and Neptune in Pisces. Once again, it is our connection to collective evolution that will be rewarded. Our growth depends on interdependence. We must leave behind victim/martyrdom scenarios. Jupiter can bring assistance, perspective, guidance, and of course—alignment with Natural Law.

4th GATE—MAY 26 2022— 24°ARIES ♈
RIGHT ACTION - PIONEERING

This Gate defines our collective evolution and we are helped or hindered by how we regulate ourselves. If we are more aligned with Mother Nature—dealing with co-creating our life on Gaia—then we may avoid drama, trauma and wake-up calls. If not, we are destined to repeat whatever we avoid learning as a species. Venus and the Moon square Pluto, create a turning point. Pioneering a healthy value system—that benefits all of humanity, and Gaia—is the only way forward.

5TH GATE—JUNE 26 2022—03 GEMINI ♊
GENERATE - ORGANIZE - DELIVER

This Gate continues to deliver on the ability to observe and make correlations. By paying attention to Natural Law, we are able to be resilient and self-empowering especially as we go through the first American Pluto return.

6th GATE—JULY 26 2022—10°CANCER ♋
RELIANCE ON OUR INNER KNOWING

Economists and historians know that civilizations face crises when resources are not shared globally and socially. As we stare down the barrel of the US Pluto return, we will be learning to love and care for each other successfully. If we are to survive as a species, we must discover new ways of sharing our precious and limited resources.

7th GATE—JULY 25 2022—17°LEO ♌
SELF-ACTUALIZING - LIVING OUR PURPOSE

Financial challenges will arise, and if you are one who shares, cares, and helps build a solid path to welcome the Age of Aquarius, the brotherhood of humankind—then this will be an opportunity to grow and change. If you have failed to learn this lesson, get ready to be whacked by a cosmic two-by-four. Massive change is indicated, but self-empowerment will be rewarded if you are committed to unity and collective evolution.

"There's power in allowing yourself to be known and heard, in owning your unique story, in using your authentic voice. And there's grace in being willing to know and hear others." Michelle Obama, Becoming

Vastu Gems 2022

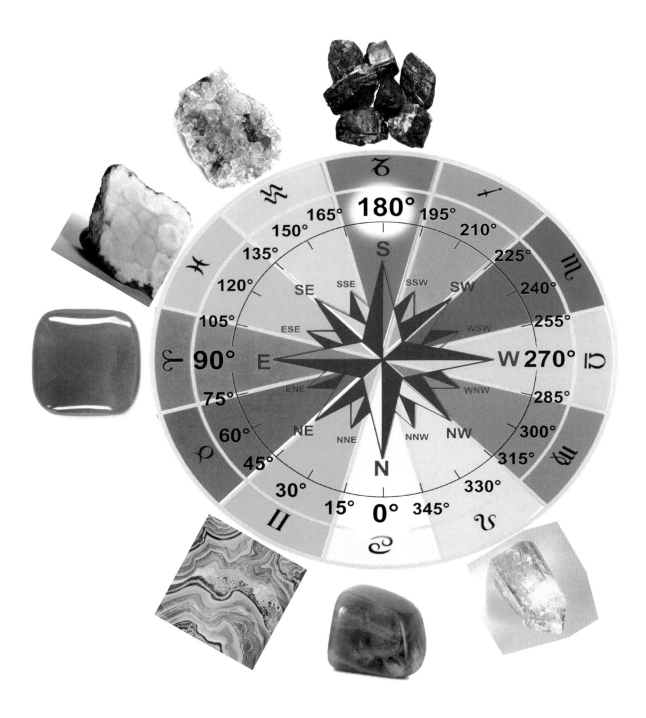

You can wear gems for the corresponding Venus gate, For example, place a Black Tourmaline, Blue Topaz, Lapis Lazuli, or Howlite in the compass area for Capricorn, as shown above, until the next Gate (see chart for dates).

Vastu hangers for each sign available through:
www.enlighteningtimes.com and www.aquarianature.com

Gate	Compass	Journal Questions	Vastu Gems
Gate 1 Capricorn	165° - 195°	Describe how you integrate warmth and dignity to overcome domination/submission scenarios.	Obsidian, Lapis Lazuli Blue Kyanite, Onyx
Gate 2 Aquarius	135°-165°	Describe how you collaborate to achieve shared goals.	Turquoise, Celestite, Angelite, Aquamarine
Gate 3 Pisces	105° - 135°	Describe how you dissolve barriers that keep you from seeing the WE of your Cosmic connectedness.	Aquamarine, Blue Kyanite, Labradorite, Quartz Crystal Seas Shells
Gate 4 Aries	75° - 105°	Describe how you trust yourself to let go in the present moment	Carnelian, Garnet, Red Chalcedony, Red Jade
Gate 5 Gemini	15° - 45°	Describe how you communicate honestly, clearly and without hesitation.	Green Jade, Malachite, Green Jasper, Aventurine
Gate 6 Cancer	345° - 15°	Describe the practices that assist you to develop healthy self-assurance.	Desert Rose, Selenite, Moonstone, Pearls, White Jade
Gate 7 Leo	330° - 345°	Describe your daily practices of creative self-expression.	Amber,Citrine, Sunstone, Yellow Quartz, Yellow Jasper, Yellow Jade

GEMS TO USE

REMEDIES

PLACEMENTS

THOUGHTS

EXPERIENCES

MORNING STAR
DESCENT OF VENUS

EVENING SET	Jan 3 2022	22°♑09'R	♀ ℞
RETROGRADE	Jan 9 2022	23°♌13'R	**INFERIOR CONJUNCTION**
MORNING RISE	Jan 14 2022	**15°♑42'R**	♀ ☌ ☉ ℞
DIRECT	Jan 29 2022	11°♑04'D	♀ D
GREATEST BRILLIANCE	Feb 09 2022	13°♑24'D	SLOWING DOWN
EVENING MAX ELONGATION	Mar 20 2022	13°♒11'D	♀ ☉ DISTANCE 45° 52'
SEVEN GATES	Feb—Aug 2022	♒	☽ ☌ ♀
MORNING SET	Sept 15 2022	12°♍28'	♀ SETS E
ES PENTAGRAM	Oct 22 2022	29°♎26'	♀ ☌ ☉ D
EVENING STAR	Dec 22 2022	19°♐46'D	

♈ Aries	♋ Cancer	♎ Libra	♑ Capricorn
♉ Taurus	♌ Leo	♏ Scorpio	♒ Aquarius
♊ Gemini	♍ Virgo	♐ Sagittarius	♓ Pisces

☌ 00 DEGREES CONJUNCTION

MORNING STAR GATES 2022
VENUS MOON CONJUNCTIONS

Morning Star	01/14/2022	15°♑ ' Rx
Descent		
Gate 1	2/27/2022	24°♑ 18'D
Gate 2	03/28/2022	21°♒ 29'
Gate 3	04/27/2022	23°♓ 21'
Gate 4	05/26/2022	28°♈ 15'
Gate 5	06/26/2022	03°♊ 53'
Gate 6	07/26/2022	10°♋ 20'
Gate 7	08/25/2022	17°♌ 26'

MORNING STAR—JOURNAL

MORNING STAR	
DESCENT	Moon Venus conjunctions
Gate 1	
Gate 2	
Gate 3	
Gate 4	
Gate 5	
Gate 6	
Gate 7	

EVENING STAR—JOURNAL

Evening Star	
Ascent	Moon Venus conjunctions
Gate 1	
Gate 2	
Gate 3	
Gate 4	
Gate 5	
Gate 6	
Gate 7	

AFTERWORD

For so many of us on Earth, the movement of Venus caught our attention in the early 2000s when the tech revolution introduced the phenomena called the "*Transit of Venus*."

This rare 1,215-year Venus event was bringing forth a New World Order. The 8 years from 2004-2012 gave us so many new tools including tablets, the Internet, and iPhones, which were just some of this millennium's Kumari Kisses.

We were able to watch the actual movement of Venus on our smart phones as She marched forward, a small black dot moving across the Sun.

As I've come to admire the depth of Evolutionary Astrology, I found we need more study on the Morning and Evening Stars in relationship to Venus's gibbous and balsamic phases. The Seven Gates are beckoning a deeper look.

How is Venus intertwined in a cosmic embrace with Pluto? How does the VPP teach more about Natural Law? How do the Seven Gates affect us personally and collectively?

I discovered that Venus' descent to the underworld actually correlates with Her being invisible in sunlight. It meant I needed to update Her ancient myths. Using my familiarity with the Monomyth, I drew some comparisons to Venus's journey through all Her stages with Joseph Campbell's Hero's Journey (see my first book, *The Mysteries of the Venus Pentagram*).

The planets speak to my Daemon Soul. A "Daemon Soul" is a person who is deeply resonant with Natural Law. Since I was a baby, I have been able to converse with the plant, gem, and animal realms.

The planets speak to all of us.

If you listen more closely to their guidance, dear reader, you may begin to speak with them once again. ☯

The Kamala Yantra - A Venus Symbol.

LINKS

TO HELP YOU EXPLORE THE MYSTERIES OF VENUS

For more information on Jeffrey Wolf Green's EA

http://schoolofevolutionaryastrology.com

http://devagreen.com

EA Glossary
http://schoolofevolutionaryastrology.com/evolutionary-astrology-books

Links to articles and videos mentioned in the book

https://www.youtube.com/watch?v=8p1CUe8w0AU

https://rosemarcus.com/rare-venus-occultation-june-56-2012/

https://astrobutterfly.com/2017/03/22/venus-conjunct-sun-a-new-venus-cycle-a-re-birth-of-the-hearth/

Find more Venus dates here:

https://www.astro.com/swisseph/ae/venus1600.pdf

http://aastl.net/FindYourVenusStarPoint.pdf

George Ozuna "Graphic Designer"
georgeozuna@sbcglobal.net

Tashi Powers "Evolutionary Astrologer"
www.enlighteningtimes.com

MORE VIDEOS FROM EA ASTROLOGER TASHI POWERS
https://www.youtube.com/results?search_query=TASHI+POWERS

Tashi Powers on RaMaTV
https://ramayogainstitute.com/teacher/tashi-powers/

Genna Howard - Gem Consultant
www.aquarianature.com

Lorena Mathendu - Text Design and Layout - CSS
mathendulorena@gmail.com

Other Essential Books by Tashi Powers

Tashi was born in a rainforest on the outskirts of Vancouver, BC. Her gifts as an astrologer were evident as early as 14-years-old, and she began reading professionally at 17. Her Venus is conjunct Jupiter on the GC axis at 28 Gemini. She has an international practice and is grateful to be able to share Natural Law with others.

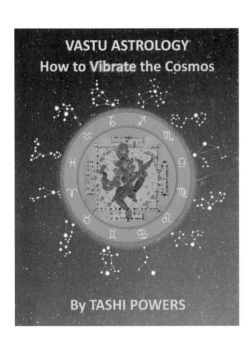

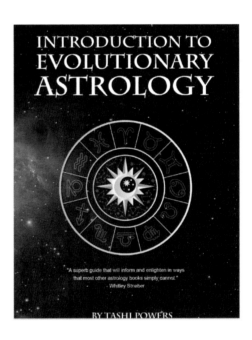

Tashi's original, practical guide on using your everyday location to attract abundance, health, and wellbeing. Drawing from both Eastern and Western world traditions including Vedic and Evolutionary Astrology, her original approach also includes treasures from feng shui, geomancy, the ley line system, and sacred compass directions—all presented in a beautifully relatable, visual format.

A Practical introduction to learn how you can make the planets, signs, and houses all work for you. Tashi offers you in-depth approach to the basic principles of EA so that you can read a horoscope, and learn the evolutionary constructs of the 12 signs.

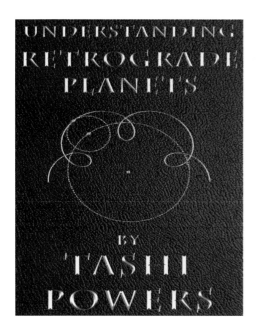

Planetary retrogrades are the Universe's way of providing us with a second chance to review and redo, revise and recreate, and remake yourself and others. Tashi's book addresses not only Mercury, but all the planets and the unique opportunities presented when they are in retrograde motion.

This forthcoming book shows how to connect your sun sign and planetary energies with healing gems and stones to create a more fulfilling, healthy life. You will learn step-by-step techniques including planetary mantras and yantras, that are personalized to help you overcome life's challenges and reach your true potential.

This is Tashi's first and now classic astrology book, which is still available in its original first edition. In its pages, she unveils at long last the Mysteries of the Venus Pentagram. This book will show you how the principles of the Venus cycle operate from her appearance as a Morning Star and also as the brightest Evening Star in our sky. You will learn how the Venus Pentagram Points take form over time and about their impact on world events and how to apply this ancient star wisdom to successfully navigate the Venus energy in your own life.

Available on Amazon
and www.enlighteningtimes.com

Made in the USA
Columbia, SC
14 April 2021